1001
Things to Find

1 jar of fairy dust

3 cute owls

2 red toadstools

4 spotty bugs

5 pretty butterflies

Fairies

igloobooks

Can you find 1001 Fairy Things?

One morning in Bluebell Wood, an enchanted owl delivers
a very important letter to Fairy Lola and Fairy Daisy.

Dear Fairy Lola and Fairy Daisy,

I have lost my magic and I desperately need your help.
There are twelve jars of fairy dust hidden in Fairyland,
just the right amount to help me get my magic back.
I would be ever so grateful if you could find them.

Fairy Queen
x

Help Lola and Daisy on an enchanted adventure through Fairyland,
as they visit lots of different fairies in search of the twelve jars of fairy dust.
There are also lots of other beautiful items to find along the way, too.

Fairy Lola

A jar of magic
fairy dust

Fairy Daisy

Let's practise first. On the opposite page, see if you can spot
Lola, Daisy and a jar of magic fairy dust. Once you've found them,
see if you can spot the items below, too.

6 vases of
flowers

10 pink
paintbrushes

16 red
apples

Rainbow Meadow

In the shimmering meadow, Lola and Daisy start their adventure and visit the rainbow fairy. The fairies are very busy collecting the pretty sparkles. Can you spot Lola, Daisy and a jar of fairy dust?

1 rainbow
fairy

4 fluffy
sheep

5 cute
unicorns

6 white
clouds

7 bottles
of perfume

8 special
cameras

9 pink
teacups

10 pairs of
cherries

13 rare
flowers

16 rainbow
nets

Enchanted Forest

In the dark wood, Lola and Daisy pay the forest fairy a visit. The little woodland fairies collect sweet nectar for their fizzy flower pop drink. Find Fairy Lola, Fairy Daisy and a jar of magic fairy dust.

1 forest fairy

4 cute birds

5 red, spotted bugs

6 woodland lanterns

7 jugs of fizzy drink

8 lilac flowers

9 spotty toadstools

10 fluttery butterflies

13 yummy muffins

16 flying fireflies

Royal Library

Shh! Lola and Daisy visit the magic library to meet the wise knowledge fairy. There are piles of pretty spell books and lots of very clever fairies everywhere. Find Lola, Daisy and a jar of fairy dust.

1 knowledge fairy

6 rolled diplomas

9 pretty globes

12 pairs of reading glasses

15 mortar board hats

Snowflakes and Skates

High up in the mountains, Lola and Daisy have come to visit the snow fairy. It's lots of fun skiing down the slopes and skating on the sparkly ice. Can you find Lola, Daisy and a jar of fairy dust?

1 snow fairy

6 skating penguins

9 snowy owls

12 mugs of hot chocolate

15 stripy scarves

Sweet Treats

Lola and Daisy are in Candy Town to meet the sweet fairy. There's a cute cupcake house, a sweetie path and yummy lollipop trees everywhere. Find Lola, Daisy and a jar of fairy dust.

1 sweet fairy

4 bird baths

5 purple wheelbarrows

6 pairs of gardening gloves

7 gingerbread men

8 candyfloss sticks

9 stripy doughnuts

10 candy trees

13 garden gnomes

16 little lollipops

Fairyland Fair

The fabulous funfair is in town, so Lola and Daisy look for the fun fairy. The fairies whirl down the slide and twirl round and round on the carousel. Spot Lola, Daisy and a jar of magic fairy dust.

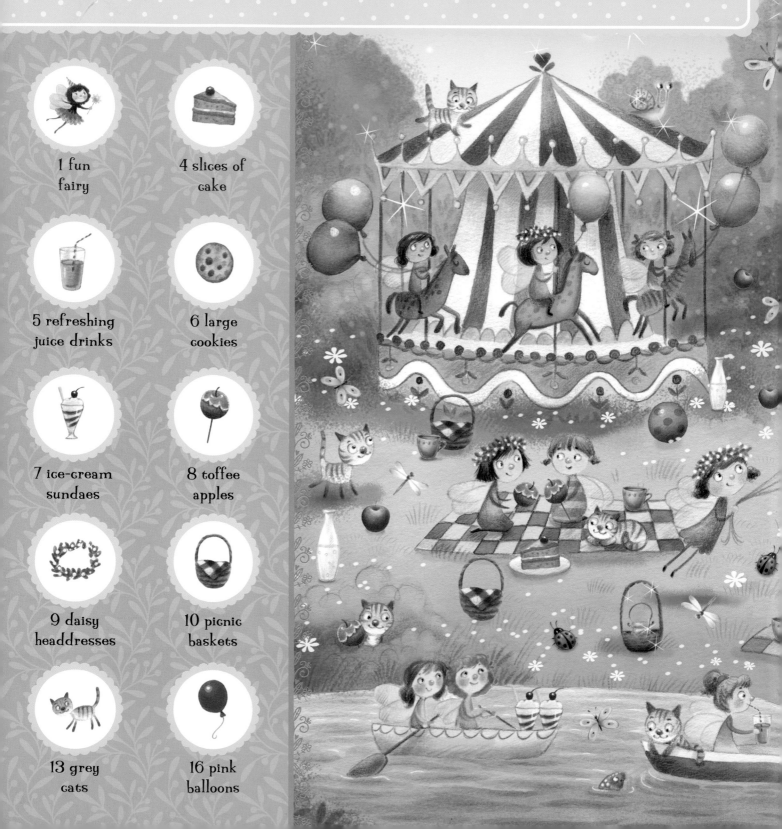

1 fun fairy

4 slices of cake

5 refreshing juice drinks

6 large cookies

7 ice-cream sundaes

8 toffee apples

9 daisy headdresses

10 picnic baskets

13 grey cats

16 pink balloons

Beach Party

Splish, splash! Lola and Daisy visit the sunshine fairy at the seaside. The fairies throw a beach party and everyone's invited. Even the snappy crabs join in the fun. Can you find Lola, Daisy and a jar of fairy dust?

1 sunshine fairy

6 stripy parasols

9 bright beach balls

12 fruity ice drinks

15 pretty shells

Flower Power

In Blossom Meadow, Lola and Daisy meet the flower fairy. The little fairies sing to the flowers to help them grow, and play games with the cute caterpillars. Can you spot Lola, Daisy and a jar of fairy dust?

1 flower fairy

6 helpful hedgehogs

9 watering cans

12 trusty trowels

15 cute caterpillars

Sparkling Spring

Time for a break! Lola and Daisy visit the water fairy at the spring. The pool fairies love to paddle, as the friendly frogs leap from lily pad to lily pad. Spot Lola, Daisy and a jar of magic fairy dust.

1 water fairy

4 mini rainbows

5 spring swings

6 large acorns

7 pink fish

8 bottles of spring water

9 round sunglasses

10 pretty lily flowers

13 friendly frogs

16 swishing dragonflies

Crystal Caves

In a glistening cave, Lola and Daisy meet the gemstone fairy. The little fairies collect twinkling crystals and jewels. Even the cute cats and bats help. Can you spot Lola, Daisy and a jar of fairy dust?

1 gemstone fairy

6 crystal statues

9 friendly bats

12 pots of crystals

15 heart-shaped jewels

Beautiful Boutique

Lola and Daisy reach the royal kingdom and visit the fashion fairy. There are lots of pretty trinkets to look at, but the fairies are only looking for one thing. Find the last jar of fairy dust, Lola and Daisy.

1 fashion fairy

6 delicate necklaces

9 coin purses

12 red hats

15 sparkly bags

The Pretty Palace

In the great royal palace, Lola and Daisy give the magnificent fairy queen the magic fairy dust. With a swish of her supreme wand, the fairy queen's magic returns! Can you find Lola and Daisy?

1 fairy queen

4 pretty chandeliers

5 royal guards

6 lovely tiaras

7 velvet cushions

8 jewel pouches

9 ruby goblets

10 trinket boxes

13 bowls of fruit

16 emerald rings

The Grand Fairy Ball

It's time to celebrate! The fairy queen is so grateful to Lola and Daisy for helping to get her magic back, that she holds the biggest ball Fairyland has ever seen. Can you spot Lola and Daisy?

3 yummy pizzas

4 little violins

5 fancy cakes

6 lost slippers

7 blue teacups

8 bottles of fruit spritz

9 royal flags

10 pretty presents

12 sweet strawberries

15 party poppers

Thank you, Lola and Daisy!

Well done! You've helped Lola and Daisy get the fairy queen's magic back.
Now see if you can find each of these enchanted characters and
items in every scene, too.

Whiskers the
fairy cat

A rare
wand

A rainbow
bird

A pretty
vanity mirror

A golden
hairbrush

A sparkly
snail

A spotty
teapot

A strawberry
cupcake

How closely were you looking at each scene? Go back and see
if you can spot these items. Each one appears only once in the book,

A fairy making
a heart necklace

A hedgehog with
a watering can

A fairy with
a diploma

An owl on
a sledge

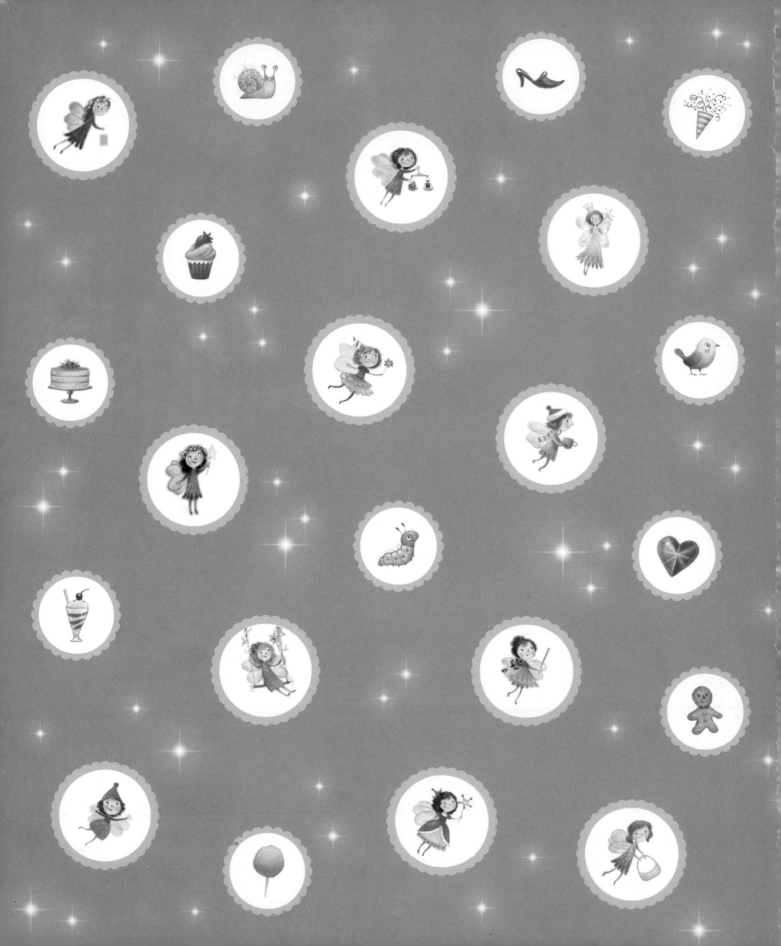